Dad's be

Dad had a beard. It was long and thick.

Mum was not a fan of the
beard. Dad's kisses hurt!
His beard was too sharp.

Mum was keen for Dad
to get rid of his beard.

"You might get nits in there," Mum said. "It will be a pain. It is best to chop it off."

"No fear!" said Dad.

"I might turn my beard red!"
Dad said with a grin. "Or
green? That will be cool."

"I might curl my beard," Dad said. "Or train it to go left and right. Now that will be a good look."

"I have bits of toast smeared in my beard," Dad said.

Yuck!

"If I need a snack, I can grab toast and jam from my beard!"

Dad shut his ears with his hands so he did not hear.

Wow! That hurts!

Dad's beard was long. He got it stuck in the zip of his jacket.

Mum had to help him get his beard out of the zip.

Then Dad went to his shed.
Nat was in the sandpit with
Meg. Meg said, "Is that
your grandad?"

"No, that's Dad," Nat said.
"Oh, my grandad has a
beard, too!" said Meg.

The next morning, Dad
cut off his beard.
"That is good," said Dad
with a grin. "I am **not**
a grandad!"

Words to blend

thick	long	brown
hurt	sharp	think
keen	might	from
turn	toast	sheep
help	wow	shed
morning	train	look

Before reading

Synopsis: Dad has a beard and Mum doesn't like it. He teases her about what he might do to it. Then one day, Nat's friend Meg says something that changes his mind.

Review phoneme/s: ar or ur ow oi

New phoneme: ear

Story discussion: Look at the cover, and read the title together. Ask: *What do you think of Dad's beard? Does he look as if he is pleased with it? What do you think other members of the family will think about it?*

Link to prior learning: Display the trigraph *ear*. Remind children that trigraphs are three letters that make one sound together. Can they read the trigraph *ear* and say the sound? Point out that *ear* is a word all on its own, but it also forms part of other words. Turn to page 4 and ask children to find and read three words with *ear*. (*beard, year, fear*)

Vocabulary check: Smeared – covered with something messy or greasy. Read page 8 together, and help children to read *smeared*, explaining if necessary that the *ed* ending makes a /d/ sound in this word.

Decoding practice: Display the words *beard, hear* and *clear*. Ask children to underline the grapheme *ear* and add dots for the other graphemes. Together, sound out and blend each word.

Tricky word practice: Display the word *my*. Ask children to circle the tricky bit (the grapheme *y* which makes the sound /igh/). Ask children to practise writing this word, and look out for it when reading.

After reading

Apply learning: Discuss the story. Can children explain what made Dad change his mind about his beard at the end? Ask: *How did Dad feel about being compared to Meg's grandad?*

Comprehension

- What are the main problems with Dad's beard, according to Mum?

- What does Mum think they should use to get rid of Dad's beard?

- How does Dad feel when he shaves off his beard at the end?

Fluency

- Pick a page that most of the group read quite easily. Ask them to reread it with pace and expression. Model how to do this if necessary.

- Turn to pages 12–13, and ask children to read Mum and Dad's speech bubbles with expression, making the two characters sound different if they can.

- Practise reading the words on page 17.

Tricky words review

of	your	was
no	my	have
you	there	said
they	be	go
oh	so	out